P9-DCC-484

Aphorisms of

DR. CHARLES HORACE MAYO
1865–1939

and

DR. WILLIAM JAMES MAYO
1861–1939

Collected by
FREDRICK A. WILLIUS, M.D.

Published by Mayo Foundation
for Medical Education and Research, 1990
Second Printing

*"Surgeons—scientists
lovers of their fellowmen"**
1929

*INSCRIPTION BY REVEREND G. P. SHERIDAN,
ROCHESTER, MINNESOTA.

FOREWORD

It is an honor and pleasure to me to have been asked by my friend and colleague, Fred Willius, to write a foreword for the collection of aphorisms he has gleaned from the writings of my father, Dr. Charlie, and my uncle, Dr. Will Mayo.

Their professional unity, their consistent loyalty to medical ideals and to each other, their constant striving to attain the best care for the patient have been and will be a source of inspiration and a model for emulation by all who knew them.

Personality differences in their individual characters but added to the strength of a perfectly matched team. Each complemented the other. One can by deduction obtain a glimpse of each by the use of the written word of each as selected by their friend and associate, Dr. Fredrick A. Willius.

Charles W. Mayo

INTRODUCTION

It was with a deep sense of responsibility that I undertook the selection and extraction of aphorisms from the writings of Dr. Charles H. Mayo and Dr. William J. Mayo. Their combined bibliographies comprise 988 written works. This accomplishment, accessory to extremely busy professional, administrative and educational duties, is almost incredible. I had read many of their works in my earlier years at the Mayo Clinic, but to reread them and to read many others was a truly inspirational experience.

About a year ago, as my investigation of the writings of these great brothers progressed, it came to my mind that the profit which I personally received from this undertaking should be shared with others. There are now many members of the staff of the Mayo Clinic and the Mayo Foundation, who through the circumstance of time, were not privileged to know the Doctors Mayo, to work with them or directly to absorb their teachings and their high ideals.

It therefore seemed desirable to record these "pearls of wisdom" in a small volume, readily accessible to the living colleagues of the Doctors Mayo, to those who did not know them and to the generations of physicians yet to come.

The traditions of a great institution should not perish, and they can only be perpetuated and augmented by authentic transmission from generation to generation. Tradition has its inception in the individuals, whose ideals, efforts, foresight and wisdom not only were creative but were sustained. Therefore, the actual words of these famous brothers, if read and remembered, should inspire their successors to appreciate more fully and to perpetuate the high standards of medical practice so magnificently exemplified by the Doctors Mayo.

Fredrick A. Willius, M.D.
ROCHESTER, MINNESOTA

APHORISMS
of
DR. CHARLES HORACE MAYO
and
DR. WILLIAM JAMES MAYO

C.H. Mayo

W. J. Mayo

Aphorisms of
DR. CHARLES H. MAYO

1. "The keynote of progress in the 20th century is system and organization,—in other words, 'team work.'"[1]

❀

2. "Carry out the two fundamental surgical requirements: see what you are doing and leave a dry field."[2]

3. "I am writing, here, not for those filled with principles, or the why, but for those still interested in technic, or the how."[3]

�֍

4. "The definition of a specialist as one who 'knows more and more about less and less' is good and true. Its truth makes essential that the specialist, to do efficient work, must have some association with others who, taken altogether, represent the whole of which the specialty is only a part."[4]

�֍

5. "Now that the first part of this meeting has been satisfactorily disposed of, we shall enter on the occasion which

brought us together, and that is the recognition of the most important event that can occur in the life of a man, that of being born."[5]

❧

6. "Long ago I learned from my father to put old people to bed only for as short a time as was absolutely necessary, for they were like a foundered horse, if they got down it was difficult for them to get up, and their strength ebbed away very rapidly while in bed."[6]

❧

7. "In the study of some apparently new problems we often make progress by reading the work of the great men of the past. . . ."[7]

8. "We live in proportion to our ability to respond to and correlate ourselves with our environment."[5]

❖

9. "In some other countries, where conditions of living are entirely different from those in the United States, problems of health have been solved by socialization of medicine but to assume that we should imitate those solutions is ridiculous."[4]

❖

10. "Today the only thing that is permanent is change."[5]

❖

11. "Examination must be within reason for the sick, or near-sick, and its

8

extent will be based on the judgment and experience of the physician."[8]

❧

12. "Medicine can be used only as people are educated to its accomplishments."[9]

❧

13. "Those of us who have passed our three score years are actually farther removed in light years of knowledge from our fathers than our fathers were removed from King Tut."[5]

❧

14. "Disease at times creates experiments that physiology completely fails to duplicate, and the wise physiologist

can obtain clues to the resolution of many problems by studying the sick."[10]

❊

15. "A surgical procedure should be planned so that the patient, with the least possible risk and loss of time, will receive the greatest possible benefit."[11]

❊

16. "It must be remembered that physicians of today are trained to treat the sick, and they must learn how to examine so-called well persons to prevent them from getting sick"[12]

❊

17. "In America our idealism is not unusual, nor does it differ much from

that of the medical faculty of other countries; if we excel in anything, it is in our
capacity for translating idealism into
action."[9]

❧

18. "We, as parents, must give up our
professed right to fix our children's
thinking."[5]

❧

19. "Judgment is a great asset; it
makes the diagnostician and the surgeon
both supermen."[13]

❧

20. "Nature and evolution dislike
waste, and whenever possible they use

tissues for other purposes when the type of structure and the form of life change."[14]

❧

21. "Probably the most interesting period of medicine has been that of the last few decades. So rapid has been this advance, as new knowledge developed, that the truth of each year was necessarily modified by new evidence, making the truth an ever-changing factor."[15]

❧

22. "The writer of textbooks should have a ready imagination and he should understand the child's mind."[16]

23. "We have still left on the earth groups of people representing every age of civilization."[17]

❊

24. "If we carry our special training too far, uneducated cults slip in."[18]

❊

25. "It took the world from the day of its creation to the time of the sixteenth century to raise a doubting Thomas of sufficient mental strength and courage to state that questions were answered not by authority, but by experiment."[5]

13

26. "It is unfortunate that so few appreciate from what small causes diseases come."[18]

❊

27. "Time has been annihilated by the telegraph, the cable, the telephone and the wireless, thus enabling the newspapers to educate the world."[5]

❊

28. "Medicine is a profession for social service and it developed organization in response to social need."[9]

❊

29. "The object of all health education is to change the conduct of in-

dividual men, women, and children by teaching them to care for their bodies well, and this instruction should be given throughout the entire period of their educational life."[8]

❧

30. "Once you start studying medicine you never get through with it."[7]

❧

31. "Of all the symptoms for which physicians are consulted, pain in one form or another is the most common and often the most urgent. Properly assessed, it stands pre-eminent among sensory phenomena of disease as a guide to diagnosis."[12]

32. "More personal hygiene and improved heredity are the keynote to the health of the coming generation."[18]

❧

33. "The coinage of the future will not alone be gold as in the past, but will grow into brains, equipment and material with controlled energy, and only on this basis can we make the necessary readjustment of all values."[5]

❧

34. "What a privilege it is to be able to teach, and how comparatively few of the many who possess the knowledge to teach are able to impart it to the student in a manner to make a permanent rather than a fleeting impression on his

mind, and at the same time arouse his interest."[16]

�

35. "Education of the masses has reached a high percentage; intellectual giants are in the minority."[5]

✿

36. "Man has taken what he wanted, dependent on strength and cunning, but he has been bettered by religion."[16]

✿

37. "Every part of the body is dependent on the whole and to develop a specialty more fully is to study what constitutes health and disease."[18]

38. "The great contribution we can make is to prepare the oncoming generations to think that they can and will think for themselves."[5]

❧

39. "When medical progress apparently lags it is often due to neglect to honour the great physicians of the past, thus neglecting to call public attention to medical progress through those who have made great achievements."[7]

❧

40. "There must be adjustment of education to the individual."[5]

❧

41. "The significance of an ailment should not be measured by the incon-

venience it causes at the time, but by
what may come of it four or five years
afterward."[12]

❧

42. "Medicine is about as big or as
little in any community, large or small,
as the physicians make it."[17]

❧

43. "The physicians, in order to stim-
ulate interest, have advocated a birthday examination to see what the audit in
the bank of health actually is."[19]

❧

44. "Probably in the not far distant
future we will crawl out of our old

methods of education, as a snake sheds its skin, and reorganize a new plan."[16]

❈

45. "When you want support for public health measures you have to educate the people. When you start to educate the people you should begin with the women because they will fight for the health of their children."[20]

❈

46. "If I were asked how the next considerable advance is to be sought and won in the field of medicine, I should say by the intimate study of the physiology and anatomy as related to symptoms, and that our first concern should

be a more extended and intimate study of pain."[12]

❧

47. "All who are benefited by community life, especially the physician, owe something to the community."[21]

❧

48. "[Study within these buildings only] plants the roots of knowledge; it does not make brains, but merely molds them and equips them for more and greater work."[22]

❧

49. "Small organs have often engaged the attention of great men,. . ."[23]

50. "Readjustment of labor will make it possible for man to develop the only thing as yet but little developed for its capacity, his highest attribute, the brain."[19]

❊

51. "While there are several chronic diseases more destructive to life than cancer none is more feared."[24]

❊

52. "The problem before us is so to exchange information, and so to educate men through travel that there shall develop a final, cosmopolitan system of medicine which will combine the best elements to be found in all countries."[25]

53. "In many years of active surgical work I have not seen death occur as the result of an unnecessary exploration."[26]

❈

54. "It would seem that the study of medicine does not always contribute to broadmindedness, as men who choose medicine as a profession are apt to lose rather than gain breadth of perception. It could be said rather that medicine develops individualism."[21]

❈

55. "Civilized man does not add to the beauties of nature, but generally destroys, perverts, or disarranges the progress of natural changes."[27]

56. "Medicine gives only to those who give, but her reward for those who serve is 'finer than much fine gold.' "[22]

❧

57. "Thus the surgeons for each period must discuss the subject and clarify it for themselves, since human experience, which affords opportunity for progress, can be passed on only to a limited extent."[28]

❧

58. "Men left the colleges with their intellectual packs on their backs to live by their own hands."[22]

❧

59. "To have better community health the people must be convinced

that certain diseases are infectious. After this conviction has become established, a community can be free from disease in proportion to what it can pay for prevention."[25]

❋

60. "We have gone on from the principle of universal opportunity to that of universal compulsion."[22]

❋

61. "The lack of money in the medical profession makes it desirable to build memorials for utility."[29]

❋

62. "The scientist is not content to stop at the obvious."[22]

63. "Let there be education in medicine commensurate to instruction; let the young physician be sound in the fundamentals, so that he may see his problem as it is, and his duty to himself, his patients and the science of medicine."[22]

❋

64. "Knowledge is acquired by a compelling force from within, by desire, or from without, by compulsion."[30]

❋

65. "One of the signs of a truly educated people, and a broadly educated nation, is lack of prejudice."[22]

66. "The trained nurse has given nursing the human, or shall we say, the divine touch, and made the hospital desirable for patients with serious ailments regardless of their home advantages."[30]

❈

67. "There are two objects of medical education: To heal the sick, and to advance the science."[22]

❈

68. "The true physician will never be satisfied just to pass his therapeutic wares over a counter."[22]

❈

69. "Anatomy and physiology will again grow in importance as living topics directly concerned in disease."[22]

70. "We are more than ever firmly convinced that war is what Sherman called it, and made of it, Hell."[31]

❀

71. "In truth, we advance far by the harmonious assembling of facts made known by many observers and writers."[32]

❀

72. "Our country is no longer isolated from other countries."[33]

❀

73. "The medical profession should feel proud of the position it has attained in the affairs of the world."[31]

74. "Good health is an essential to happiness, and happiness is an essential to good citizenship."[34]

❧

75. "The soldier is rewarded or promoted for risk of life and personal valor; an officer who is given authority to command the destruction of life may have spent but a few months in a training camp, while the medical officer who is responsible for the preservation of life devotes many years to preparation."[33]

❧

76. "Democracy is not achieved in a day."[31]

77. "In the study of digestion as a necessary function in the maintenance of life, one comes very close to the fundamental question of life itself."[35]

❊

78. "There are lots of people who think they are sick and who are not sick."[34]

❊

79. "A crowned tooth is not a 'crown of glory' and may cover a multitude of germs."[36]

❊

80. "Obedience to law means life and liberty."[31]

81. "It is a poor government that does not realize that the prolonged life, health and happiness of its people are its greatest asset."[33]

❈

82. "More good would come to our country through tongue control than birth control."[31]

❈

83. "The laws of civilization signify progress and efficiency along scientific lines."[33]

❈

84. "The by-products of human deficiencies, mental, moral and physical, are a clog and a burden to the state."[31]

85. "Experience with success or failure only enables the individual operator to justify methods."[37]

❋

86. "It will soon be generally recognized that the citizen is best made when a child."[31]

❋

87. "Life does not occur without life."[34]

❋

88. "From a medical standpoint we must be proud of our country and our great dead."[31]

89. "Public demand is the only true stimulus for tradesmen and professional men alike."[33]

❧

90. "In medical progress the means of relief by therapeutic measures or surgery have far outstripped our knowledge of the cause of disease."[38]

❧

91. "The government has dabbled in medical affairs at enormous expense for what has been accomplished."[33]

❧

92. "The philosophic view of bacteria is to consider them necessary to life as the minute chemists of the air, the water, and the soil."[38]

93. "Science and education have done much but education still lags."[34]

❊

94. "As a profession we are probably less acute in our general observation than was the practitioner of the old school."[1]

❊

95. "Health has come to be generally recognized as an economic principle."[39]

❊

96. "We make many laws but obey few; and having an abhorrence of discipline, we discuss freedom."[40]

❊

97. "The sooner patients can be removed from the depressing influence of

general hospital life the more rapid their convalescence."[1]

�֍

98. "Nothing endures unless it is of use in the world and in the economy of nature."[40]

✖

99. "The prevention of disease today is one of the most important factors in the line of human endeavor."[41]

✖

100. "In the conquering of serious diseases by surgical measures it is important that the operation itself should be as free from mortality as possible."[43]

101. "The choice of an anesthetic is more often determined by the idiosyncrasy of the operator than the necessity of the case."[44]

❊

102. "The small expense of restoring an individual to health and usefulness is returned manifold."[45]

❊

103. "The people will gradually demand more of their medical advisers."[41]

❊

104. "Much of the fog which surrounded the early-day knowledge of this subject was due to a nomenclature which labeled the syndrome of symptoms with the names of various men who

more or less perfectly described the condition."[42]

❈

105. "The fact that these fads exist may be fortunate since it leads the advocates to redouble their efforts in a desire to prove the efficiency of the method."[46]

❈

106. "It has been the constant effort of the medical profession to cure or control disease by a study of its causes."[47]

❈

107. "While medicine is a science, in many particulars it cannot be exact, so baffling are the varying results of varying conditions of human life."[48]

REFERENCES

CHARLES HORACE MAYO

1. The Examination, Preparation and Care of Surgical Patients. *Journal-Lancet, 36:*1–4 (Jan. 1), 1916.
2. Splenomegaly. *Collect. Papers Mayo Clin. & Mayo Found., 27:*555–566, 1935.
3. Wrinkles and Recipes in Intestinal Surgery. *Ann. Surg., 98:*830–834 (Nov.), 1933.
4. Surgery's Problems as They Affect the Hospital. *Mod. Hosp., 51:*68–69 (Sept.), 1938.
5. Tomorrow's Education Seen by Dr.

References

Mayo. *Northwestern University Alumni News*, *10*:17–19 (July), 1931.

6. The Old and the New in Prostatic Surgery. *Ann. Surg.*, *100*:883–886 (Nov.), 1934.

7. Surgery of the Sympathetic Nervous System. *Ann. Surg.*, *96*:481–487 (Oct.), 1932.

8. When Does Disease Begin? Can This Be Determined by Health Examination? *Minnesota Med.*, *15*:40–42 (Jan.), 1932.

9. International Medical Progress. *Collect. Papers Mayo Clin. & Mayo Found.*, *23*:1020–1024, 1931.

10. La función del higado en relación con la cirugía. *An. de cir.*, *2*:120–129 (Apr.), 1930.

11. Surgery of the Hepatic and Common Bile Ducts. *Collect. Papers Mayo Clin. & Mayo Found.*, *22*:93–102, 1930.

12. The Influence of Pain and Mortality in Modern Medical Practice. *Proc. Interst. Postgrad. M. A. North America*, Oct. 19–23:245–248, 1931.

13. Renal and Ureteral Stone. *Internat. J. Med. & Surg.*, *42*:613–615 (Dec.), 1929.

14. Contributing Causes of Genito-urinary Anomalies. *Surg., Gynec. & Obst.*, *48*:367–371 (Mar.), 1929.

15. Philosophic Considerations of the Gall-bladder. *Ann. Surg.*, *92*:640–643 (Oct.), 1930.

16. Educational Development of Man. *Collect. Papers Mayo Clin. & Mayo Found.*, *20*:937–942, 1928.

17. Focal Infection in Chronic and Recurring Diseases. *Univ. Toronto M. J.*, (Apr.), 1928.

18. The Interdependence of Medicine and Dentistry. *J. Am. Dent. A.*, *15*:2011–2017 (Nov.), 1928.

19. Insurance as a Factor in Health Better-

ment. *Collect. Papers Mayo Clin. & Mayo Found., 20:*951–956, 1928.

20. Preventive Medicine. *Texas State J. Med., 24:*403–405 (Oct.), 1928.

21. The Value of Broadmindedness. *M. Life, 34:*165–167 (Apr.), 1927.

22. Problems in Medical Education. *Collect. Papers Mayo Clin. & Mayo Found., 18:*1093–1102, 1926.

23. Hepatic Function in Health and Disease. *Surg., Gynec. & Obst., 42:*9–14, 1926.

24. Carcinoma of the Right Segment of the Colon. *Ann. Surg., 83:*357–363 (Mar.), 1926.

25. Preventive Medicine. *Collect. Papers Mayo Clin. & Mayo Found., 28:*1190–1192, 1936.

26. The Cause and Relief of Acute Intestinal Obstruction. *J. A. M. A., 79:*194–197 (July 15), 1922.

27. Avian Tuberculosis in Man. *South. M. J., 19:*29–34, 1926.

28. The Appendix in Relation to, or as the Cause of, Other Abdominal Diseases. *J. A. M. A., 83*:592–593 (Aug. 23), 1924.

29. Jerome Cochran Lecture: The Thyroid and Its Diseases. *Collect. Papers Mayo Clin. & Mayo Found., 14*:427–433, 1922.

30. The Trained Nurse. *Collect. Papers Mayo Clin. & Mayo Found., 13*:1242–1244, 1921.

31. War's Influence on Medicine. Presidential Address. *J. A. M. A., 68*:1673–1677 (June 9), 1917.

32. The Cancer Problem. *Canad. M. A. J., 8*:786–790, 1918.

33. Educational Possibilities of the National Medical Museum; in the Standardization of Medical Training. *J. A. M. A., 73*:411–413 (Aug. 9), 1919.

34. The Relation of Mouth Conditions to General Health. *J. Am. Dent. A., 6*:505–512 (June), 1919.

References

35. The Treatment of Peptic Ulcer by Gastro-enterostomy. *Minnesota Med.*, 2:1–4, 1919.

36. Problems of Infection. *Minnesota Med.*, 1:414–416, 1918.

37. The Thyroid and Its Diseases. *Surg., Gynec. & Obst.*, 32:209–213 (Mar.), 1921.

38. Stone in the Kidney. *Ann. Surg.*, 7:123–127, 1920.

39. The Value of Public Health Service. *Pub. Health*, 4:533–535, 1916.

40. Medical Service in the United States Army. *St. Paul M. J.*, 19:351–353, 1917.

41. Constitutional Diseases Secondary to Local Infections. *Dental Rev.*, 27: 281–297, 1913; *Collect. Papers Mayo Clin. & Mayo Found.*, 17–34, 1913.

42. Ligation of the Thyroid Vessels in Certain Cases of Hyperthyroidism. *Ann. Surg.*, 50:1018–1024 (Dec.), 1909.

43. A Consideration of the Mortality in One Thousand Operations for Goi-

ter. *Surg., Gynec. & Obst., 8*:237–240 (Mar.), 1909.

44. Goiter. With Preliminary Report of Three Hundred Operations on the Thyroid. *J. A. M. A., 48*:273–277 (Jan. 26), 1907.

45. Discussion Original Paper, "The University Hospital," by Dr. C. L. Greene. *Collect. Papers Mayo Clin. & Mayo Found.*, 556–557, 1911.

46. The Present Status of the Treatment of Fractures. *Railway Surg. J., 18*:400–410, 1911–1912; *Collect. Papers Mayo Clin. & Mayo Found.*, 484–495, 1911.

47. Observations on the Thyroid Gland and Its Diseases. *Surg., Gynec. & Obst., 14*:363–368 (Apr.), 1912; *Collect. Papers Mayo Clin. & Mayo Found.*, 439–450, 1911.

48. President's Address. *Collect. Papers Mayo Clin. & Mayo Found.*, 601–604, 1905–1909.

Aphorisms of

DR. WILLIAM J. MAYO

❧

1. "Surgery is more a matter of mental grasp than it is of handicraftsmanship."[1]

❧

2. "We have never been allowed to lose sight of the fact that the main purpose to be served by the Clinic is the care of the sick."[2]

3. "American practice is too broad to be national. It had the scientific spirit, and science knows no country."[3]

❦

4. "It is worth-while to secure the happiness of the patient as well as to prolong his life."[4]

❦

5. "Property rights have heretofore been considered sacred; human rights, of less consequence."[5]

❦

6. "At the close of a man's life, to estimate his worth it is wise to see him in relation to his life surroundings, to know not only the part he played as an individual, but also as a component part

of the great events to which he contributed in the betterment of mankind."[6]

7. "Reading papers is not for the purpose of showing how much we know and what we are doing, but is an opportunity to learn."[2]

8. "How much better it is to have the walls covered with books with which we are establishing friendly relations, than with pictures of passing interest which we have happened to obtain. Eventually pictures may lose their interest, whereas books never lose their fascination."[7]

9. "Experience is the great teacher; unfortunately, experience leaves mental scars, and scar tissue contracts."[8]

❖

10. "The school house is the proud monument to the desire of the people that their children shall receive a better education than they themselves had."[10]

❖

11. "I think all of us who have worked years in the profession understand that many very skillful operators are not good surgeons."[1]

❖

12. "It never occurred to us that we could be anything but doctors."[7]

13. ". . . . the highly scientific development of this mechanistic age had led perhaps to some loss in appreciation of the individuality of the patient and to trusting largely to the laboratories and outside agencies which tended to make the patient not the hub of the wheel, but a spoke."[6]

⚜

14. "Instruction from teachers and books teaches a man what to think, but the great need is that he should learn how to think."[10]

⚜

15. "Sometimes I wonder whether today we take sufficient care to make a thorough physical examination before our patient starts off on the round of

the laboratories, which have become so necessary that oftentimes we do not fully appreciate the value of our five senses in estimating the condition of the patient."[7]

❧

16. "Have we thought enough of wisdom, which moves knowledge and makes it useful?"[10]

❧

17. "It is for the younger people to meet the conditions of their generations in the way that appears to them to be wise and best."[10]

❧

18. "He never tried to utter the final word."[9]

19. "We think of truth as something that is invariable, but add a new circumstance and we have a new truth."[10]

❧

20. "To children is given the power of readily acquiring languages; later, mathematics is acquired with the same readiness; but reasoning from cause to effect is a development of adolescence and early manhood."[8]

❧

21. "Education must concern itself with the aspirations and needs of the common man."[10]

❧

22. "Commercialism in medicine never leads to true satisfaction, and to

maintain our self-respect is more pre-
cious than gold."[7]

✣

23. "It is a man's duty to provide
moderately for his family, but anything
beyond this may be a detriment to his
descendants."[10]

✣

24. "The wit of science not only
expresses but actually reveals the science and art of medicine."[8]

✣

25. "When people have entered the
seventies of their age, they usually find
themselves growing conservative."[10]

26. "Given one well-trained physician of the highest type he will do better work for a thousand people than ten specialists."[8]

❧

27. "We cannot turn back the hand of time in disease, but early operation will give a low mortality and cure a higher percentage of patients than has been cured in the group which I have considered here."[11]

❧

28. "[of Dr. John B. Murphy]..., his was not the nature that desired praise, but with the divine spark he desired ever to kindle new fires under old misconceptions."[12]

29. "The foundation of modern gastric surgery was the exploratory incision."[13]

❀

30. "Unfortunately, only a small number of patients with peptic ulcer are financially able to make a pet of an ulcer."[14]

❀

31. "Civilization and intellectual growth depend largely on preventive medicine."[15]

❀

32. "It has been said that the anatomist never made a good surgeon, that it was the pathologist who made the surgeon."[16]

33. "I have been surprised to note the readiness with which high-grade young men, graduates from medical institutions which are models for our time, yield to the temptation of machine-made diagnosis."[13]

❧

34. "Of all cooperative enterprises public health is the most important and gives the greatest returns."[15]

❧

35. "No person, regardless of whether or not he has money, is refused good medical attention."[18]

❧

36. "Medicine is the best of all professions, the most hopeful."[19]

37. "The outstanding feature of American public life today is reverence for education."[20]

❧

38. "People die from very real things."[22]

❧

39. "Since the object of travel is primarily self-improvement, time should not be wasted looking for things done badly and for things to criticize."[21]

❧

40. "Individually, no man is respected more highly than the physician."[17]

41. "Youth has visions of the future which are not shared to an equal extent by those of middle and later age; youth is a builder of images, a dreamer of dreams."[20]

❧

42. "That which can be foreseen can be prevented."[23]

❧

43. "The old should remember that they represent the past, and that the young represent the future."[20]

❧

44. "The reputation of a surgeon, in the final analysis, must rest upon (1)

originality, (2) teaching by word of mouth, (3) teaching by the printed word and (4) surgical judgment, and operative skill."[24]

❧

45. "Competitive medicine was the response of the individual physician to his training and environment."[25]

❧

46. "Knowledge is static; wisdom is active and moves knowledge, making it effective."[20]

❧

47. "The surgeon is often intolerant and the internist self sufficient."[23]

48. "These heroic men whose life work marked epochs in medicine we think of as individuals, but what they accomplished singly was perhaps of less importance than the inspiration they gave to the group of men who followed them."[26]

❧

49. "After all, the best the college can do is to give the students breadth of knowledge, not necessarily depth of knowledge."[20]

❧

50. "If there is a sixth sense, it is intuition, that instinctive summing up of memories and other evidences collected by the special senses and correlated in man's consciousness."[27]

51. "The physician has been the council for the prosecution and the defense, the jury and the judge."[25]

❉

52. "When knowledge is translated into proper action we speak of it as wisdom."[28]

❉

53. "As we become more civilized we are beginning to emphasize not the differences that lead to antagonism but the common impulses and desires which lead to better understanding."[20]

❉

54. "Age carries mental scars left by experience which shorten vision, but age carries wisdom."[20]

55. "It is a great thing to make scientific discoveries of rare value, but it is even greater to be willing to share these discoveries and to encourage other workers in the same field of scientific research."[29]

❧

56. "In the autumn of life one perhaps may be privileged to become reminiscent."[30]

❧

57. "Individually the American is the most efficient man on earth; collectively and politically, extraordinarily inefficient."[25]

58. ". . . it is better to think and some-times think wrong than not to think at all."[31]

❧

59. "As a nation we see that we must raise the average level of intelligence, if we are to have good government, because the average intelligence controls the form of government."[32]

❧

60. "Today, it is impossible for any one man to know more than a little of comparatively few things."[33]

❧

61. "Every teacher was a practitioner of medicine and every student was taught to practice medicine."[30]

62. "When one thinks of knowledge, books and other evidences of the development of the civilization of man come first to mind."[34]

❧

63. "It has been said, and I believe justly, that one should go to the educator for information but not for advice."[30]

❧

64. "The examining physician often hesitates to make the necessary examination because it involves soiling the finger."[35]

❧

65. "There is no excuse today for the surgeon to learn on the patient."[30]

66. "The mere possession of a diploma does not endow one with extraordinary knowledge on all possible medical subjects."[33]

�֍

67. "As I look back on these men who influenced me so greatly, I realize that their influence lay not in their craftsmanship, but in their high qualities of mind."[36]

✖

68. "One of the chief defects in our plan of education in this country is that we give too much attention to developing the memory and too little to developing the mind; we lay too much stress on

acquiring knowledge and too little on the wise application of knowledge."[32]

❈

69. "Interpretation of the pathology of the living is the outstanding feature of modern medicine."[34]

❈

70. "We think of truths as ponderables capable of being measured and weighed, but introduce a new fact or a new thought and a new truth is developed."[37]

❈

71. "Our emotions and capacity for acquiring knowledge are hereditary."[38]

72. "The keen clinician, as he grows in experience, becomes more and more valuable as age advances."[39]

73. "The romance of medicine lies in inductive philosophy, in which tomorrow is the great day."[40]

74. "Democracy had its birth in the failure of autocracy."[37]

75. "Democracy is safe only so long as culture is in the ascendency, . . ."[37]

76. "The future of any country depends on the proper use of its most intelligent men."[41]

77. "Medical science aims at the truth and nothing but the truth."[42]

❋

78. "One meets with many men who have been fine students, and have stood high in their classes, who have great knowledge of medicine but very little wisdom in application. They have mastered the science, and have failed in the understanding of the human being."[43]

❋

79. "The hospital should be a refuge to which the sick might go for relief as they went before our Savior, . . ."[44]

❋

80. "Rehabilitation is to be a master word in medicine."[45]

81. "Truth is a constant variable."[46]

❁

82. "The church and the law deal with the yesterdays of life; medicine deals with the tomorrows."[43]

❁

83. "The ills of today must not cloud the horizon of tomorrow."[44]

❁

84. "I look through a half opened door into the future, full of interest, intriguing beyond my power to describe, but with a full understanding that it is for each generation to solve its own problems and that no man has the wisdom to guide or control the next generation."[46]

68

85. "The university, through its organized intelligence, controls the future."[44]

❄

86. "The sciences bring into play the imagination, the building of images in which the reality of the past is blended with the ideals for the future, and from the picture there springs the prescience of genius."[45]

❄

87. "One must confess that whatever his mental and moral deficiencies, and they are certainly great, as a machine, man has no equal."[47]

88. "Perhaps the ability not only to acquire the confidence of the patient, but to deserve it, to see what the patient desires and needs, comes through the sixth sense we call intuition, which in turn comes from wide experience and deep sympathy for and devotion to the patient, giving to the possessor remarkable ability to achieve results."[48]

❧

89. "It is easy to philosophize; the philosopher is said to be one who bears with equanimity the sufferings of others."[20]

❧

90. "Books become friends that never fail; . . ."[49]

91. "[of Dr. Lewis Linn McArthur] As a surgeon he never grew old, but was interested and interesting to the end."[48]

❧

92. "Out of this composite education we finally accept the idea that man does not live for himself alone but as an integral part of society."[20]

❧

93. "To books we turn to learn of the past, opinions of the present, and prognostications of the future."[49]

❧

94. "A prominent specialist in gastrointestinal diseases once asked, 'How is it possible that you, a general surgeon, see so many of these cases while I, who

am devoting all my time to this work, see so few?' I could only answer, 'The thickness of the abdominal wall prevents you from seeing them.' "[50]

❧

95. "This country rightfully has based its ideal of a safe democracy on education."[51]

❧

96. "It is interesting to speculate as to what diagnoses were made in the cases of duodenal ulcer prior to our present knowledge."[50]

❧

97. "The independent thinker is a crank if he thinks wrongly, but a genius if he thinks rightly."[52]

98. "The spleen is an organ of contradiction and mystery: in health of relatively unimportant function, in disease a menace of grave import."[53]

❀

99. "Science is organized knowledge of the physical world."[52]

❀

100. "Modern medicine may be said to have begun with the microscope."[54]

❀

101. "The man of science in searching for the truth must ever be guided by the cold logic of facts, and be animated by scientific imagination."[52]

102. "The educator has assumed almost full charge of medical education."[54]

❧

103. "Life is largely a matter of chemistry."[55]

❧

104. "There is a limit to the amount of learning a man can absorb."[56]

❧

105. "We must bear in mind the difference between thoroughness and efficiency. Thoroughness gathers all the facts, but efficiency distinguishes the two-cent pieces of non-essential data from the twenty-dollar gold pieces of fundamental fact."[54]

106. "Memory can be spoken of as mental photography."[52]

❈

107. "The glory of medicine is that it is constantly moving forward, that there is always more to learn."[56]

❈

108. "The aim of medicine is to prevent disease and prolong life; the ideal of medicine is to eliminate the need of a physician."[56]

REFERENCES

WILLIAM JAMES MAYO

1. Master Surgeons of America; Frederic S. Dennis. *Surg., Gynec. & Obst.,* 67:535–536 (Oct.), 1938.
2. The Value of the Weekly General Staff Meeting. *Proc. Staff Meet., Mayo Clin.,* 10:70–72 (Jan. 30), 1935.
3. The Influence of European Surgery on American Practice. *St. Paul M. J.,* 16:601–605, 1914.
4. Diagnostic Fog. *Proc. Staff Meet., Mayo Clin.,* 12:159–160 (Mar. 10), 1937.
5. Surgery in Relation to Life Insurance. *Journal-Lancet,* 112:146–150, 1914.

References

6. Edward Martin, M.D., 1859-1938. *Collect. Papers Mayo Clin. & Mayo Found.*, *30*:919–921, 1938.

7. Discussion of Paper by T. E. Keys Entitled "The Medical Books of William Worrall Mayo, Pioneer Surgeon of the American Northwest." *Collect. Papers Mayo Clin. & Mayo Found.*, *30*:938–943, 1938.

8. In the Time of Henry Jacob Bigelow. *J. A. M. A.*, *77*:597–603 (Aug. 20), 1921.

9. The Work of Dr. Henry S. Plummer. *Proc. Staff Meet., Mayo Clin.*, *13*:417–422 (July 6), 1938.

10. The Establishment of "The Mayo Foundation House" and Its Purpose. *Proc. Staff Meet., Mayo Clin.*, *13*:553–554 (Aug. 31), 1938.

11. Splenectomy in Splenic Anemia and Banti's Disease. *J. A. M. A.*, *77*:34–36 (July 2), 1921.

12. The Surgical Significance of Hepatic

Incompetency. *Surg., Gynec., & Obst., 33:*463–469 (Nov.), 1921.

13. Radical Operations on the Stomach With Especial Reference to Mobilization of the Lesser Curvature. *Surg., Gynec. & Obst., 36:*447–453 (Apr.), 1923.

14. Progress in the Handling of Chronic Peptic Ulcer. *J. A. M. A., 79:*19–22 (July 1), 1922.

15. Socialization of Medicine and of Law. *Collect. Papers Mayo Clin. & Mayo Found., 11:*1157–1165, 1919.

16. The Relation of Anatomy to Present-day Surgery. *J. A. M. A., 74:*367–369, 1920.

17. The Doctor and His Patient. *Hygeia,* 7:347–350, 1929.

18. Nursing and Hospital Costs for Individuals in Moderate Circumstances. *Collect. Papers Mayo Clin. & Mayo Found., 21:*1035–1038, 1929.

19. Remarks in Accepting Honorary Mem-

bership in the Southern Surgical Association. *Collect. Papers Mayo Clin. & Mayo Found.*, *24:*1051–1054, 1937.

20. Education Guides the Young to Good Citizenship. *Minnesota Med.*, *19:*468–470 (July), 1936.

21. Observations on South America. *J. A. M. A.*, *75:*311–315 (July 31); 377–378 (Aug. 7); 475–477 (Aug. 14); 540–541 (Aug. 21); 606–607 (Aug. 28); 672–673 (Sept. 4), 1920.

22. Procedures Following Nephrectomy. *J. A. M. A.*, *64:*953–957 (May 20), 1915.

23. Mortality and End Results in Surgery. *Surg., Gynec. & Obst.*, *32:*97–102 (Feb.), 1921.

24. Dr. John B. Murphy—an Appreciation. *Surg., Gynec. & Obst.*, *23:* (Between pages 236-237), 1916.

25. The Medical Profession and the Public.

J. A. M. A., *76*:921–925 (Apr. 2), 1921.

26. An Address on the Relation of the Basic Medical Sciences to Surgery. *Canad. M. A.. J.*, *17*:652–657 (June), 1927.

27. The Relative Value of the Special Senses to the Surgeon. *Ann. Surg.*, *86*:1–5 (July), 1927.

28. Presidential Address. *Surg., Gynec. & Obst.*, *30*:97–99, 1920.

29. Remarks on the Romance of Medicine. *Proc. Staff Meet., Mayo Clin.*, *10*:393–394 (June 19), 1935.

30. Medical Education for the General Practitioner. *J. A. M. A.*, *88*:1377–1379 (Apr. 30), 1927.

31. Remarks Before the Association. (Abstr.) *Collect. Papers Mayo Clin. & Mayo Found.*, *27*:1212–1216, 1935.

32. The Economic Relation of the University System to the Development of a Social Democracy. *Collect. Papers*

Mayo Clin. & Mayo Found., *25*: 1105–1107, 1933.

33. Specialization in Surgery. *Arch. Surg.*, *10*:264–266, 1925.

34. In Medicine Understanding Must Come Before Belief. *Bull. M. Coll. Virginia*, *27*:3–15 (Mar.), 1930.

35. The Cancer Problem. *Journal-Lancet*, *35*:339–343 (July 1), 1915.

36. Masters of Surgery in the Early Years of the Annals of Surgery. *Ann. Surg.*, *81*:3–8 (Jan.), 1925.

37. The Debt of the University Graduate. *Collect. Papers Mayo Clin. & Mayo Found.*, *16*:1226–1230, 1924.

38. Recent Contributions of Medical Men to Surgical Progress. *J. A. M. A.*, *95*:644–647 (Aug. 30), 1930.

39. Observations on the Sympathetic Nervous System. *Brit. M. J.*, *2*:627–628 (Oct. 18), 1930.

40. Diverticula of the Sigmoid. *Ann. Surg.*, *92*:739–743 (Oct.), 1930.

41. The Function of the University Concerns the Tomorrows, the Function of the Government, the Yesterdays and Todays. *Collect. Papers Mayo Clin. & Mayo Found.,* *16*:1223–1225, 1924.

42. The Influence of Ignorance and Neglect on the Incidence and Mortality of Cancer. *J. Indiana M. A.,* *17*:331–334, 1924.

43. The Preliminary Education of the Clinical Specialist. *Collect. Papers Mayo Clin. & Mayo Found.,* *23*:1001–1005, 1931.

44. The Teaching Hospital of the University of Michigan. *J. Michigan M. Soc.,* *25*:9–12 (Jan.), 1926.

45. Contributions of Pure Science to Progressive Medicine. *J. A. M. A.,* *84*:1465–1469 (May 16), 1925.

46. Seventieth Birthday Anniversary. *Ann. Surg.,* *94*:799–800 (Oct.), 1931.

47. The Relation of the Spleen to Certain

Anemias. *J. Indiana M. A.,* 8:499–504 (Nov.), 1915.

48. Lewis Linn McArthur. *Surg., Gynec. & Obst.,* 60:883–885 (Apr.), 1935.

49. Libraries Useful in Their Day. *Bull. M. Library A.,* 25:70–72 (Sept.), 1936.

50. Chronic Duodenal Ulcer. *J. A. M. A.,* 64:2036–2040 (June 19), 1915.

51. "Useful in Its Day." *Proc. Staff Meet., Mayo Clin.,* 10:1–5 (Jan. 2), 1935.

52. Perception. *Collect. Papers Mayo Clin. & Mayo Found.,* 20:997–1006, 1928.

53. The Enlarged Spleen. *South. M. J.,* 21:13–16 (Jan.), 1928.

54. Looking Backward and Forward in Medical Education. *J. Iowa M. Soc.,* 19:41–46 (Feb.), 1929.

55. The Advancement of Learning in Medicine Through Biochemistry. *Indust. & Engin. Chem.,* 20:457–460, 1928.

56. The Aims and Ideals of the American Medical Association. *J. Nat. Education A.,* 158–163, 1928.

APPENDIX I

So-called Lost Oration by Dr. W. J. Mayo Before a
Committee of the Minnesota State Legislature on
March 22, 1917.

*In 1917 a bill was introduced into the
Minnesota State Legislature for an act to
instruct the Board of Regents of the University of Minnesota to dissolve the affiliation of the Graduate School of the
university with the Mayo Foundation
for Medical Education and Research.
This affiliation had been established by
the Board of Regents on June 9, 1915.
On the night of March 22, 1917, Dr.*

Appendix I

Mayo appeared before the Senate Committee on Education which was conducting public hearings on the bill. His extemporaneous remarks, set down only by the newspaper reporters present, were so powerful and so eloquent that support for the bill subsided rapidly, and it never became an act. Dr. Mayo used no manuscript. The version which follows is reproduced from the Minneapolis Morning Tribune, *March 23, 1917, by special permission of the* Minneapolis Star and Tribune Company.

I had some hesitancy in appearing at this meeting. There has been much misunderstanding and misapprehension about the whole plan. So that you may understand just what my brother and I desire to do, let me go back to our boyhood days.

My father, Dr. W. W. Mayo, was recognized as the leading physician and surgeon of Southeastern Minnesota. When we were small boys we assisted him as much as we could, gradually growing into the profession much as a farmer boy learns by working with his father.

Now my father had certain ideals. He believed that any man who had physical strength, intellectual capacity or unusual opportunity held such endowments in trust to do with them for others in proportion to his gifts.

As our business grew, my brother and I added men to the staff, not as hired men, but as co-workers. We have had our ideals. Everyone who came into the clinic and hung up his hat was to get treatment regardless of the cost and no one was asked if he had the price.

Because erroneous statements have been made in this regard, I will say that we have never charged a physician or a clergyman or any dependent member of the family of either.

As we grew larger, we took in young men and finally built up a school and provided fellowships to enable students of exceptional ability to work and study in connection with the clinic. We had 26 of those fellowship students in 1914, before the arrangement with the University.

In 1898 my father retired and we took what money we had and turned it over to Burt W. Eaton, a fellow townsman, with instructions to look after it and such additions as we might make. Last year it totaled about $1,500,000. It is the basis of the endowment of the foundation.

We have never taken notes at the clinic. No mortgage has ever been given on a home to pay a bill there. We never sue. Thirty per cent of our patients are charity cases. About 25 per cent pay barely the cost of treatment.

I can't understand why all this opposition should have been aroused over the affiliation with the University. It seems to be the idea of some persons that no one can want to do anything for anybody without having some sinister motive back of it.

If we wanted money, we have it. That can't be the reason for our offer. We want the money to go back to the people who gave it to us. The proposal for this affiliation came from the University to us and did not originate with us. We want to serve the state that has given us so much and we think the best way we can serve it is through medical education.

The offer of the endowment fund of the foundation when the affiliation becomes permanent is an outright tender despite the talk of a "phantom gift" which has been heard through the state. I know that doctors of Minnesota two years ago were appealed to in letters containing misrepresentations.

Now let's call a spade a spade. This money belongs to the 2,500,000 people in this state. I don't care two raps whether the medical profession of the state like the way this money has been offered for use. It wasn't their money. Discussions against the affiliation have been in the past of just such petty and trivial detail as we have heard tonight.

I have always thought a good deal of Lincoln's Gettysburg address. There's a line in it which explains why we want to do this thing. It is "that these dead shall not have died in vain." We know how hard it is for those who have had the misfortune of deaths in their families, of deaths that might have been avoided. What better could we do than take young men and help them to become proficient in the profession so as to prevent needless deaths?

We are willing to change the contract at the end of the trial period, if that is thought wise. If your committee will come to Rochester, we will show you what is being done and what the arrangement means. My brother and I are over 50 years old. What better can we do than devote our remaining years to this work?

APPENDIX 2

A Letter from Doctor William J. Mayo to the
University of Minnesota, written on February
15, 1934

*In the year 1934, Dr. W. J. Mayo and
Dr. C. H. Mayo added another $500,000
to the endowment of the Mayo Foundation for Medical Education and
Research, which is one part of the Graduate School of the University of Minnesota. This gift was accompanied by the
following letter, signed by Dr. William
J. Mayo.*

As a man advances in years, he begins to look backward over those conditions and happenings in the past that influenced his life work. To grow up in a doctor's family with a professional background of some generations will likely have, as it did with my brother and myself, that sort of influence which leads, not to conscious choice of medicine as a career, but rather to unconscious elimination of every other choice. Neither my brother nor I ever had an idea of being anything but a doctor.

Our father recognized certain definite social obligations. He believed that any man who had better opportunity than others, greater strength of mind, body, or character, owed something to those who had not been so provided; that is, that the important thing in life is not to accomplish for one's self alone, but for each to carry his share of collective responsibility. Stepping as we did into a large general practice, with a great deal of surgery from the beginning, my brother and I had an exceptional opportunity, as we entered medical practice during the early period of development of asepsis and antisepsis in surgery which had come through the work of Pasteur and Lister, this opportunity was unique. We were especially fortunate that we had the benefit of our father's large experience to help us apply the modern methods to replace the old type of surgery which up to this time had been practised. There being two of us, with absolute mutual confidence, each of us was able to travel at home and abroad each year for definite periods of study of subjects connected with surgery, as well as to attend meetings, while the other was at home carrying on the practice.

In 1894, having paid for our homes and started a modest life insurance program, we decided upon a plan whereby we could eventually do something worthwhile for the sick. This plan was to put aside from our earnings any sums in excess of what might be called a reasonable return for the work we accomplished. It seemed to us then, as now, that moneys which should accumulate over and above the amount necessary for a living under circumstances which would give favorable conditions to work and to prepare reasonably for our families, would interfere seriously with the object that we had in view.

Contented industry is the mainspring of human happiness. Money is so likely to encourage waste of time, changing of objectives in life, living under circumstances which put one out of touch with those who have been life-long friends, who perhaps have been less fortunate. How many families have we seen ruined by money which has taken away from the younger members the desire to labor and achieve and has introduced elements into their lives whereby, instead of being useful citizens, they have become wasteful and sometimes profligate.

Medicine constantly became more complex. From time to time new members were added to the staff. Each member of the staff received a salary which was sufficient to permit wholehearted attention to his work. There was no profit-sharing—accumulations over and above the amount necessary for the purposes I have outlined were conservatively invested, and have been reinvested, adding all interest to principal.

Year by year more young physicians applied for positions as assistants and internes in the hospitals. The need of providing in some way a better form of post-graduate medical education for these earnest young men soon became apparent.

In 1907 I was honored by an appointment to the Board of Regents of the University of Minnesota. During these twenty-seven years I have had the privilege and responsibility of becoming intimately acquainted with the work of the University. This association has been an inspiring influence, bringing me into contact with university presidents of wide vision, representative men and women on the Board of Regents, and able and experienced administrators, devoted to the University and the welfare of the state. I have found a capable and growing faculty in each college of the University, and have been impressed by these loyal men and women who are giving their lives to investigations, to teaching, and to public service. It seems to my brother and myself that the crowning endeavor of a life in medicine would be to aid in the development of medical education and research.

Our state University is not political in origin or management. Yet it comes from and belongs to the people. The representatives of the people at intervals, elect a continuing board of twelve members each for a term of six years. The members of the Board of Regents have always been representative citizens, eminently fitted for their responsibility in safeguarding the interests of education, and I have been impressed with their sympathetic understanding of the changing economic and social conditions. The Regents are responsive to the public voice, but not to public clamor.

Foundations which depend on self-continuing bodies of trustees may do well for the first and second generation, but there is the hazard that in later periods new trustees who are unfamiliar with the spirit and ideals of the founders may through lack of understanding defeat their purpose. Especially is there danger in laying down inflexible rules and regulations which may hamper and even obstruct the original purpose of the Foundation. However, the control and management of the University of Minnesota, which places the responsibility for its institutions in the hands of each succeeding generation, furnishes ideal conditions for perpetuation of broadly outlined trusts and purposes.

The fund which we had built up and which had grown far beyond our expectations had come from the sick, and we believed that it ought to return to the sick in the form of advanced medical education, which would develop better trained physicians, and to research to reduce the amount of sickness. My brother and I came to the conclusion that this purpose could be best accomplished through the state University.

In 1913, when our fund seemed to be of sufficient size to warrant the endowment of a foundation at the University of Minnesota to carry out our purposes, we proposed the affiliation. After careful consideration, the arrangements were agreed upon, June 9, 1913. My brother and I gave to the University of Minnesota a million and a half dollars, which was the entire fund which we had been able to accumulate up to that time, to found the Mayo Foundation for Medical

Education and Research, with the understanding that the sum should reach two millions or more before any part of the income should be expended. September 13, 1917, the temporary arrangement became a permanent affiliation, and the results have shown the wisdom of the course pursued.

Our relations with the University of Minnesota and its Medical School have been most cordial. The graduate students in medicine who have come to the University and through the University to Rochester for graduate medical instruction make a splendid roster. Before the Mayo Foundation for Medical Education and Research was established, there had been at the Clinic in Rochester 105 internes, special students, or assistants, 41 of whom are now in university positions. The 36 students of this category who were in Rochester at the beginning of the Foundation, became fellows. Of the more than 1,350 men and women who have studied in the Mayo Foundation for Medical Education and Research, more than 450 are in responsible teaching positions in medical schools in this country and abroad.

In order to care for additional funds which had been accumulating since the affiliation with the University in 1915, the Mayo Properties Association, a charitable corporation without capital stock, was formed on October 8, 1919, under a thirty-year charter from the state of Minnesota which was later by legislative enactment made a perpetual charter.

The Mayo Properties Association holds title to all the lands, buildings, laboratories, and equipment of all kinds and description used in Rochester in the work of the Mayo Foundation. This Association also owns and handles the moneys accrued for the same purposes as the endowment of the Mayo Foundation for Medical Education and Research, for future disposal. These moneys and properties never can inure to the benefit of any individual.

Nineteen years have gone by since the Mayo Foundation for Medical Education and Research was established. The association between the University and the Foundation at Rochester has been most harmonious, and has been distinguished by splendid co-operation on both sides for the benefit of higher medical education and research. The people's money, of which we have been the moral custodians, is being irrevocably returned to the people from whom it came.

The practice of medicine in Rochester is carried on in the same manner as by other members of the regular medical profession throughout the state and nation. All classes of patients, without regard to race or creed, social or financial standing, receive necessary care without discrimination. The income from the Mayo Foundation funds can be used only for medical education and research as approved by the administration of the University, and ordered by the Board of Regents.

The affiliated hospitals in Rochester

are approved by the American College of Surgeons. While under the medical direction of our staff, the hospitals are independently owned and managed.

The trustees of the Mayo Properties Association are in entire accord with our plans, and therefore at this time they unanimously have authorized our proposal to transfer $500,000 from the Mayo Properties Association to add to the endowment of the Mayo Foundation for Medical Education and Research.

Very truly yours,

SIGNED: *William J. Mayo*

The University of Minnesota's Acknowledgement
of Dr. William J. Mayo's letter.

Seldom in anyone's lifetime does the
opportunity come to read a document as
sincere, mature in philosophy, and yet
unpretentious, as the letter written by
Dr. William J. Mayo, in behalf of himself
and his brother, Dr. Charles H. Mayo, to
accompany the recent gift of $500,000
from the Mayo Properties Association to
the University of Minnesota. Composed
by a man who has been honored in every
part of the world, it reveals the heart and
thought of one at the peak of his profession who has never lost touch with the
simple verities of life, or in achieving
success failed to appreciate his obligations to his profession and the society in
which he practiced it.

Dr. Mayo's letter contains, along with its splendid personal philosophy, a statement of the duties of wealth, an expression of the importance of education, and an embodiment of the highest ideals in the practice of medicine. In it he puts into words the spirit that has been expressed tangibly in the gifts of $2,500,000 by himself and his brother to the Mayo Foundation for Graduate Medical Study and Research. With the idea of giving wider circulation to so fine a human document, the University of Minnesota is putting Dr. Mayo's letter into print.

L. D. Coffman,
PRESIDENT

WILLIUS, FREDRICK A., (1888-1972), B.S., M.D., M.S. in Medicine, F.A.C.P., was born November 24, 1888, at St. Paul, Minnesota; received the degree of B.S. in 1912 and of M.D. in 1914 from the University of Minnesota; and was an intern at the University Hospital, Minneapolis, from 1914 to 1915. He entered Mayo Foundation as a Fellow in Medicine July 1, 1915. He was appointed first assistant July 1, 1916, and associate January 1, 1920. He received the degree of M.S. in Medicine in 1920 from the University of Minnesota. He was a former head of a section on cardiology, Mayo Clinic, and associate professor of medicine, Mayo Foundation. He was a fellow of the American College of Physicians and a member of the Southern Minnesota Medical Association, the American Medical Association, the American Congress of Internal Medicine, the American Heart Association, the Minnesota Heart Association (president, 1925), the Central Society for Clinical Research, the Interurban Clinical Club, the Alumni Association of Mayo Foundation, Phi Rho Sigma, and Sigma Xi. He was married to Stella M. Popple September 26, 1917.